The Heart of
Messiah

George Frideric Handel
A Performing Edition by Colin Hand

Kevin Mayhew

6.45

We hope you enjoy the music in this book. Further copies are available from your local music shop or Christian bookshop.

In case of difficulty, please contact the publisher direct by writing to:

The Sales Department
KEVIN MAYHEW LTD
Rattlesden
Bury St Edmunds
Suffolk
IP30 0SZ

Phone 01449 737978
Fax 01449 737834

Please ask for our complete catalogue of outstanding Church Music.

The text of Messiah was compiled from Scripture by Charles Jennens (1700-1773)

First published in Great Britain in 1995 by Kevin Mayhew Ltd

© Copyright 1995 Kevin Mayhew Ltd

ISBN 0 86209 668 5
Catalogue No: 1450034

Front Cover: *Feed My Sheep* by Walter Crane (1845-1915).
Reproduced by courtesy of Christchurch, Streatham, Lambeth/
Bridgeman Art Library, London.
Cover design by Veronica Ward and Graham Johnstone.

Music Editor: Anthea Smith
Music setting by Chris Hinkins

Contents

The organ arrangement in this edition may be used alone or in combination with other instruments.

Instrumental parts for use with this edition are also available from the Publisher.

Violin 1
Violin 2
Viola
Cello / Bass
Timpani

COLIN HAND studied the organ with Dr Melville Cook and held church appointments in North Lincolnshire and Sheffield, England. He spent fifteen years as a lecturer in Music at Boston College followed by a similar period as an examiner for Trinity College of Music, London. He has a research doctorate in early Tudor church music and is the author of *John Taverner, His Life and His Music (Eulenburg, 1977)*. Dr Hand is a prolific composer and arranger in almost every form.

Foreword

Handel's oratorio, *Messiah,* was written in the astonishingly short space of twenty-two days in August and September of 1741. It was first performed in the Musick Hall, Fishamble Street, Dublin, in April the following year, since when it has surely become the best-loved and widest performed of any work in the choral repertoire.

In its entirety the piece lasts for about two and a half hours; the aim in *The Heart of Messiah* was to produce a shortened version of the work, but one that would retain the essence of the original, both musical and textual. This edition lasts about one and a half hours and provision has been made for an interval (after the Chorus 'His yoke is easy') if desired.

Admittedly, no abbreviated version can satisfy everyone, and some well-known, well-loved movements have been omitted. So too have the second sections of some of the *da capo* arias, in any case a common practice today. It is hoped, however, that *The Heart of Messiah* still embodies the musical and literary message of the original within a more manageable length.

The vocal parts are the original throughout, but a new organ part has been written, based upon Handel's orchestral score, that lies comfortably under the hands and feet, at the same time providing sufficient support for the voice parts. Inevitably, this has involved a certain amount of 'pruning' where the thicker orchestral textures occur, but, after all, Handel himself was not averse to tailoring his (and other people's) scorings to suit the occasion and the forces available at the time.

COLIN HAND

THE HEART OF MESSIAH

George Frideric Handel (1685-1759)

A Performing Edition by Colin Hand

Sinfonia
Overture

Recitative
Comfort ye my people

saith your God. Speak ye com-for-ta-bly to Je-ru-sa-lem, speak ye com-for-ta-bly to Je-ru-sa-lem, and cry un-to her, that her war - fare, her war - fare is ac-com-plished, that her i - ni - qui-ty is

Man.

Ped.

B

par-doned, that her i - ni - qui - ty is par - doned.

The voice of him that cri - eth in the wil - der - ness, 'Pre - pare ye the way of the Lord, make straight in the de - sert a high - way for our God.'

Man. Ped.

Gt. 8'4'

Air
Ev'ry valley shall be exalted

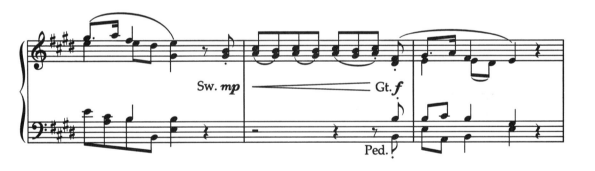

shall be ex-al-ted, shall be ex-al - - ted, shall be ex-al - - ted, shall be ex-al - - ted, and ev'ry

Gt. *f* Sw. *mp* Man. Ped.

Gt. *f* Sw. *mp*

Gt. *f* Sw. *mp* Man.

and the rough pla-ces plain.

Gt. *f*

f

Ev-'ry val-ley,   ev-'ry val-ley

C

(Sw.) *mf*   Gt. *f*   Sw.

shall be ex-al

15

the croo - ked straight,   the

croo - ked straight,   the croo - ked straight, and the rough pla - ces plain,

Ped.

and the rough pla - ces plain,   and the rough pla - ces

plain,   the

cresc.   Gt. *mf*

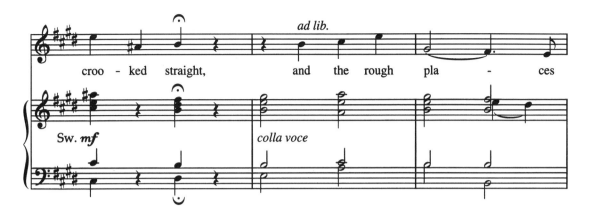

croo - ked straight, and the rough pla - ces

plain.

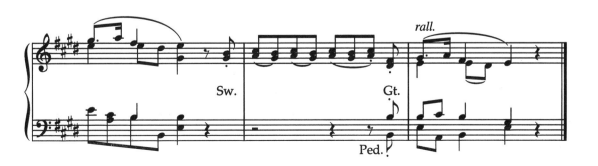

Chorus
And the glory of the Lord

Where the text '-ry of' is to be sung to one note, the two syllables should be run together.

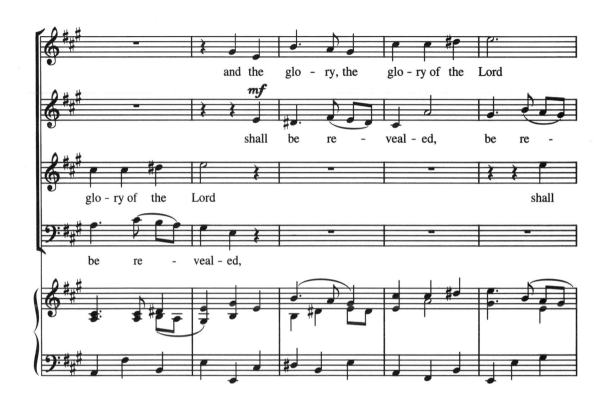

glo - ry, the glo - ry of the Lord shall be re - veal - ed,

glo - ry, the glo - ry of the Lord shall be re - veal - ed,

glo - ry, the glo - ry of the Lord shall be re - veal - ed,

glo - ry, the glo - ry of the Lord shall be re - veal - ed,

mf

and all flesh shall

mf

Man.

ge - ther, for the mouth of the

- ge - ther, and all flesh shall

spo - ken it, and all flesh shall

spo - ken it, and all flesh shall

Lord hath spo - ken it,

see it to - ge - ther, and all flesh, and all flesh shall

see it to - ge - ther, and all flesh shall see it to -

see it to - ge - ther,

Man.

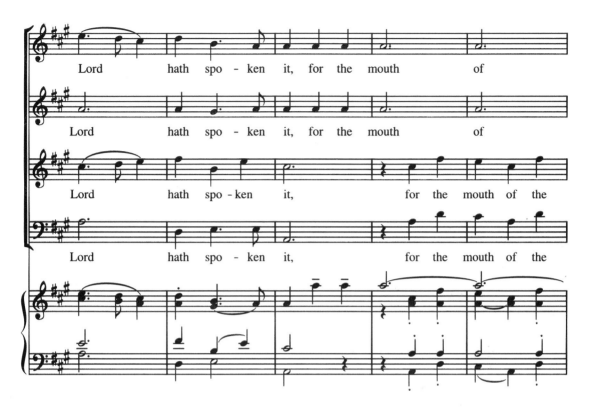

Lord hath spo - ken it, for the mouth of

Lord hath spo - ken it, for the mouth of

Lord hath spo - ken it, for the mouth of the

Lord hath spo - ken it, for the mouth of the

the Lord hath spo - ken it.

the Lord hath spo - ken it.

Lord, the mouth of the Lord hath spo - ken it.

Lord, the mouth of the Lord hath spo - ken it.

Adagio

ff

Recitative
Behold, a virgin shall conceive

Be -hold, a vir -gin shall con -ceive, and bear a son,

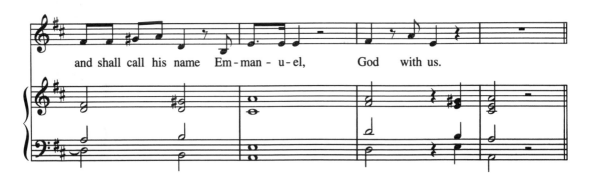

and shall call his name Em -man - u - el, God with us.

Air and Chorus
O thou that tellest good tidings to Zion

O thou that tell - est good ti - dings to Je - ru - sa - lem, lift up thy voice with strength, lift it up, be not a - fraid; say un - to the

rise,   a - rise,   a - rise, shine, for thy light is come,

and the glo - - - ry of the Lord,   the

glo - ry of the Lord   is

G

mp

36

God! be - hold, the glo - ry of the

God! be - hold, the glo - ry of the

God! be - hold, the glo - ry of the

God! be - hold, the glo - ry of the

Lord is ri - sen u - pon thee. O

Lord is ri - sen u - pon thee. O

Lord is ri - sen u - pon thee. O

Lord is ri - sen u - pon thee. O

thou that tell - est good ti - dings to Zi - on, say un - to the ci - ties of

thou that tell - est good ti - dings to Zi - on, say un - to the ci - ties of

thou that tell - est good ti - dings to Zi - on, say un - to the ci - ties of

thou that tell - est good ti - dings to Zi - on, say un - to the ci - ties of

Ju - dah, be - hold, be - hold, the

Ju - dah, be - hold, be - hold, the

Ju - dah, be - hold, be - hold, the

Ju - dah, be - hold, be - hold, the

glo - ry of the Lord, of the Lord, the

glo - ry of the Lord, of the Lord, the glo - ry of the

glo - ry of the Lord, of the Lord, the

glo - ry of the Lord, of the Lord, the

glo - ry of the Lord is ri - sen u - pon thee.

Lord is ri - sen u - pon thee.

glo - ry of the Lord is ri - sen u - pon thee.

glo - ry of the Lord is ri - sen u - pon thee.

Recitative

For behold, darkness shall cover the earth

rise   u - pon thee,   and his

glo -   ry shall be seen u - pon thee,   and his

glo -   ry shall be seen   u - pon thee.   And the gen - tiles shall

come   to thy light,   and kings   to the bright - ness   of   thy ris - ing.

Air
The people that walked in darkness

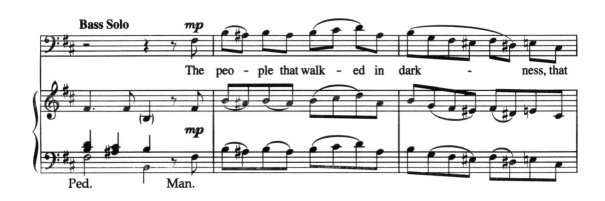

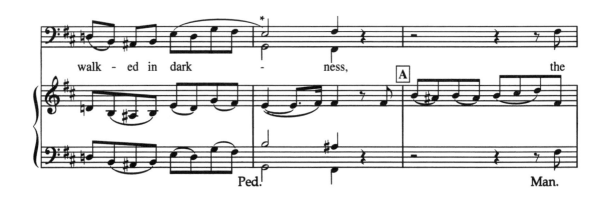

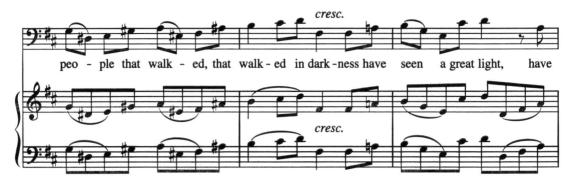

* Handel provided two versions: the singer should choose the most convenient.

seen a great light, the peo - ple that walk - ed, that

(or Ped.)

walk - ed in dark - ness have seen a great light,

Ped.

the peo - ple that walk - ed, that walk - ed in dark - ness, that

Man.

walk - ed in dark - ness, the peo - ple that walk - ed in

dark - - ness have seen a great light, have

seen a great light, a great light have

seen a great light:

and they that dwell, that dwell in the land of the

sha - dow of death, and

they that dwell, that dwell in the land, that dwell in the land of the

sha - dow of death, u -

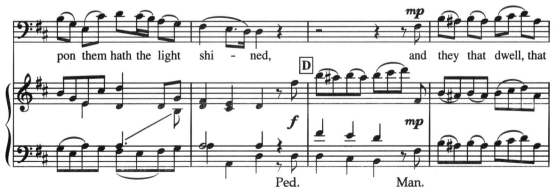

pon them hath the light shi - ned, and they that dwell, that

dwell in the land of the sha - dow of death,

u - pon them hath the light

shi - ned, u - pon them hath the light shi - ned.

Ped.

Man.

Ped.

rall.

Chorus
For unto us a child is born

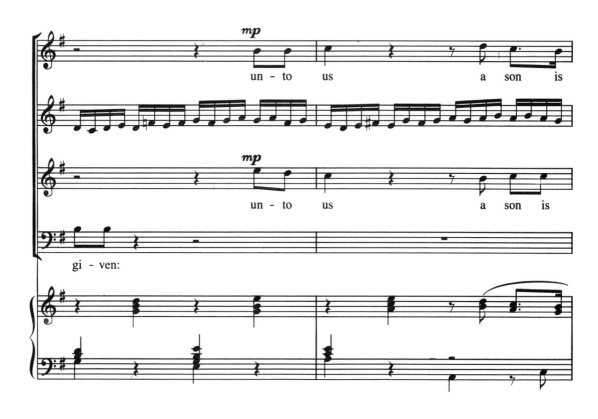

gi - ven:

gi - ven:

gi - ven: and the go - vern-ment shall be u - pon his shoul -

mf

mf

and the go-vern-ment shall be u-pon his shoul - der;

and the go-vern-ment shall

mf

- der;

and the go-vern-ment shall

mf

mf

Prince of Peace.

Prince of Peace.

Prince of Peace.

Prince of Peace.

rall.

Pifa (Pastoral Symphony)

* If a quiet 4' stop is not available, manual parts should both be played an octave higher with 8' tone alone.

Recitative
There were shepherds abiding in the field

Soprano Solo

There were shep-herds a-bid-ing in the field, keep-ing

watch o-ver their flocks by night.

Andante

And Man.

lo, the an-gel of the Lord came u-pon them, and the glo-ry of the

Lord shone round a-bout them: and they were sore a-fraid.

attacca

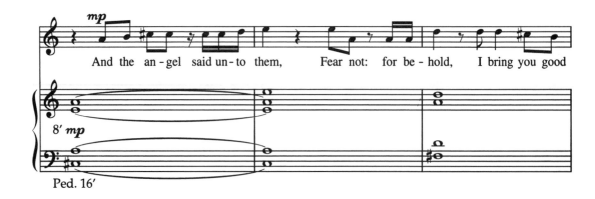

And the an-gel said un-to them, Fear not: for be-hold, I bring you good

ti-dings of great joy, which shall be to all peo-ple.

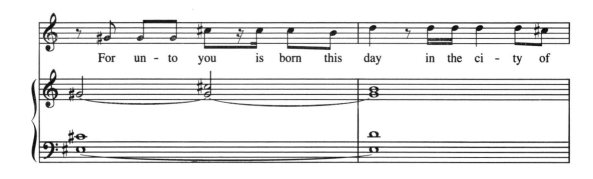

For un-to you is born this day in the ci-ty of

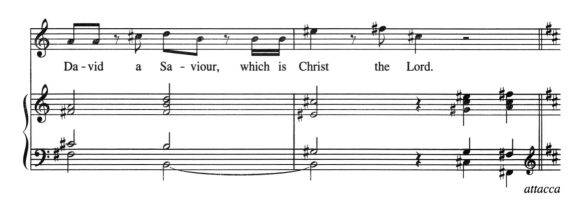

Da-vid a Sa-viour, which is Christ the Lord.

attacca

Chorus
Glory to God

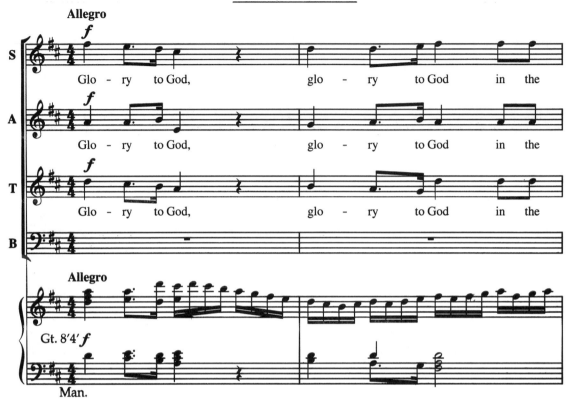

glo - ry to God in the high - est,

glo - ry to God in the high - est,

glo - ry to God in the high - est, and

mf

and

Ped.

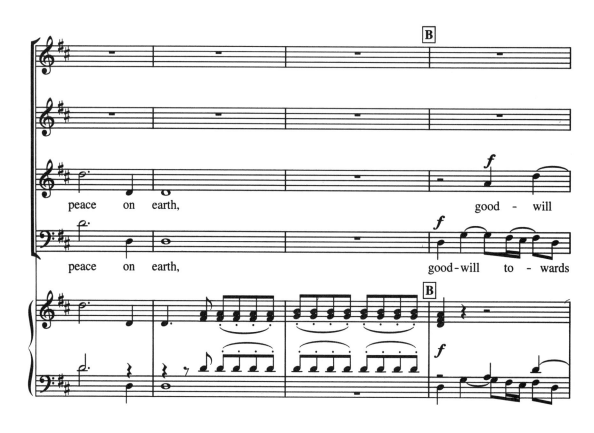

peace on earth, good - will

peace on earth, good - will to - wards

good - will to - wards men, good - will to -

good - will to-wards men, good - will

good - will to-wards men, good - will

good - will to - wards men, good - will

- wards men.

to - wards men.

to - wards men.

to - wards men.

Man.

mf   *dim.*   *mp*   *p*

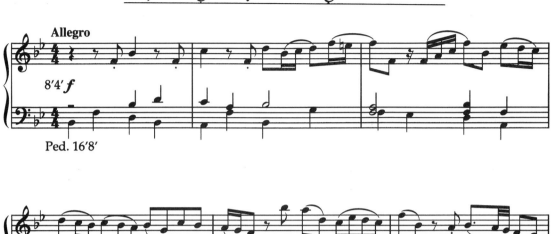

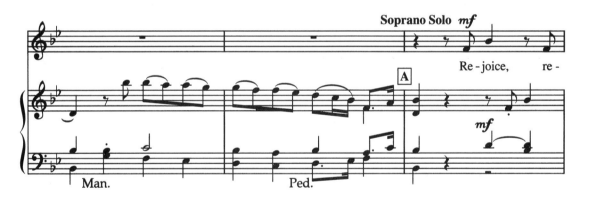

O daugh-ter of Zi - on!

O daugh-ter of Zi -on! re-joice, re-joice,

re-joice,

Man.

Ped.

He is the righ - teous Sa - viour, and he shall speak peace un- to the hea - then, he shall speak peace, he shall speak

then.

Re-joice, re-joice, re-joice

great-ly,

re-joice

great-ly,

O daugh - ter of Zi - on!

Then shall the eyes of the blind be opened

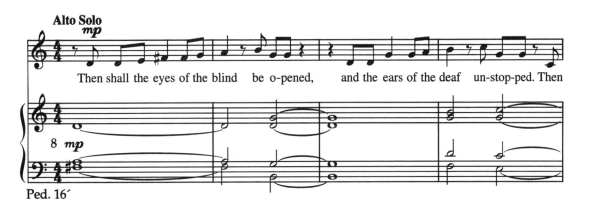

Alto Solo

Then shall the eyes of the blind be o-pened, and the ears of the deaf un-stop-ped. Then

Ped. 16'

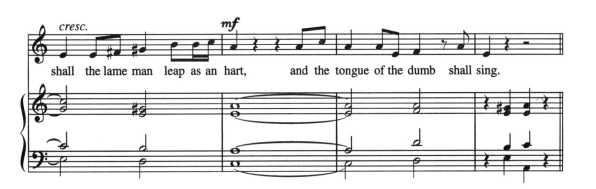

shall the lame man leap as an hart, and the tongue of the dumb shall sing.

Air
He shall feed his flock

Larghetto

He shall feed his flock like a

shep - herd, and he shall ga - ther the lambs with his arm,

ye that la - bour, come un - to him, ye that are hea - vy la - den, and

he will give you rest.

D

Take his yoke u-pon you, and

learn of him, for he is meek and low - ly of heart, and

ye shall find rest, and ye shall find rest un - to your souls.

Take his yoke u-pon you, and learn of him, for he is meek and low-ly of heart, and ye shall find rest, and ye shall find rest un-to your souls.

Chorus
His yoke is easy, his burthen is light

His yoke is ea - sy, his bur-then is

Man. (or Ped. ad lib.)

light, his bur-then, his bur - then is light,

His

His yoke is ea -

yoke is ea - sy, his bur-then is light,

sy, his bur-then is light, his bur-then is light, his

His yoke is ea -

Ped.

his bur-then is light, his bur-then, his

his bur - then is light,

bur-then, his bur-then, his bur - then is light, is light,

sy, his bur-then, his bur - then is light,

Man.

bur - then is light, his bur - then, his bur - then is light,

his bur - then is light,

his bur - then is light, is light,

his bur - then, his bur - then is light, his yoke is

Ped. Man.

his yoke is ea - sy, his

his bur - then is light, his bur - then, his

ea - sy, his

Ped.

bur-then, his bur - then, his bur - - - then is

light, his bur-then is light, his bur - - then is

light, is light, his bur - - then is

light, is light, his bur - - then is

Ped.

D

light, his yoke is ea - sy, and his bur - then is

light, his yoke is ea - sy, his yoke is ea - sy, his bur-then is

light, his yoke is ea - sy, is ea - sy, his bur-then is

light, his yoke is ea - sy, is ea - sy, his bur-then is

D

light, his yoke is ea - sy, his bur - then is light, his yoke

light, his yoke is ea - sy, his bur - then is light, his yoke

light, his yoke is ea - sy, his bur - then is light, his yoke

light, his yoke is ea - sy, his bur - then is light, his yoke

is ea - sy, and his bur - then is light.

is ea - sy, and his bur - then is light.

is ea - sy, and his bur - then is light.

is ea - sy, and his bur - then is light.

Man (or Ped. ad lib.)

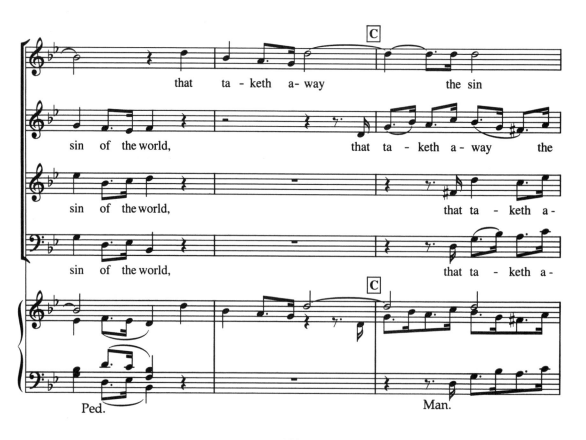

Ped.   Man.

Air
He was despised

jec - ted of men, a man of sor - rows,

a man of sor rows, and ac -quain-ted with grief,

a man of sor - rows, and ac - quain - ted with grief.

He

sor-rows, and ac-quain-ted with grief, and ac-quain-ted with grief,

a man of sor-rows, and ac-quain-ted with grief.

Chorus
<u>Surely he hath borne our griefs</u>

borne our griefs, and car - ried our sor - rows,

borne our griefs, and car - ried our sor - rows,

borne our griefs, and car - ried our sor - rows,

borne our griefs, and car - ried our sor - rows,

sure - ly, sure - ly he hath borne our griefs, and

sure - ly, sure - ly he hath borne our griefs, and

sure - ly, sure - ly he hath borne our griefs, and

sure - ly, sure - ly he hath borne our griefs, and

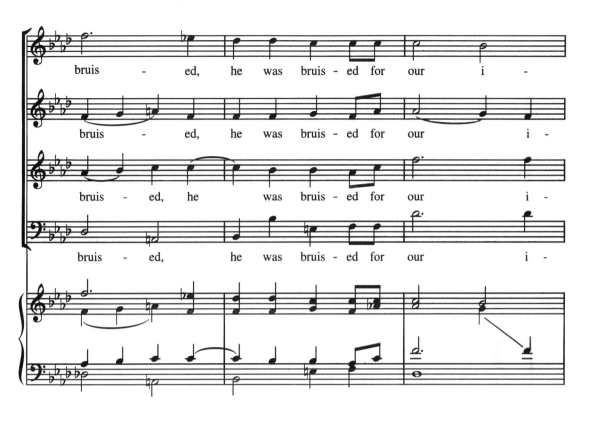

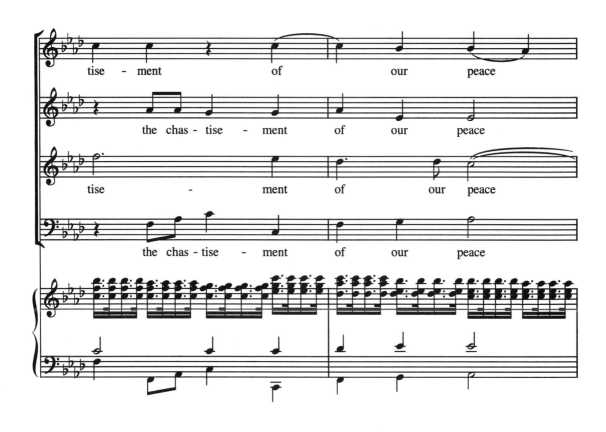

tise - ment   of   our   peace

the chas - tise - ment   of   our   peace

tise - ment   of   our   peace

the chas - tise - ment   of   our   peace

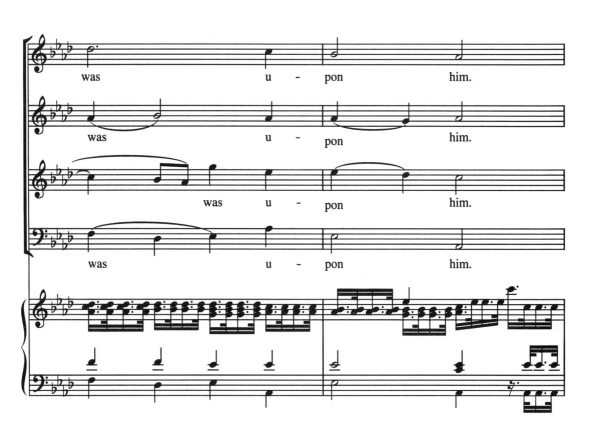

was   u - pon   him.

was   u - pon   him.

was   u - pon   him.

was   u - pon   him.

Thy rebuke hath broken his heart

Largo
Tenor Solo

Thy re - buke hath bro - ken his heart; he is full of

Sw. 8' *p*

Ped. 16

hea - vi - ness, he is full of hea - vi - ness; thy re - buke hath

bro - ken his heart, he look - ed for some to have pi - ty on

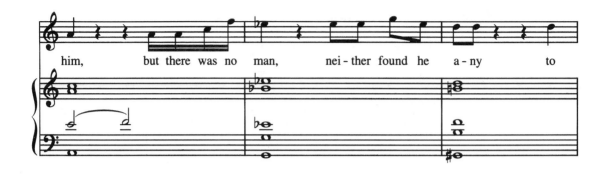

him, but there was no man, nei-ther found he a-ny to

com - fort him, he look - ed for some to have pi - ty on him,

but there was no man, nei-ther found he a-ny to com - fort him.

Air

Behold, and see

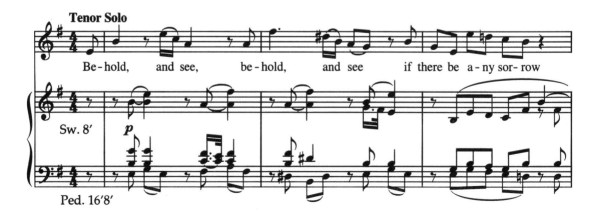

Tenor Solo

Be-hold, and see, be-hold, and see if there be a-ny sor-row

Sw. 8′

p

Ped. 16′8′

like un-to his sor-row, be-

hold, and see if there be a-ny sor-row like un-to his sor-row, be-

hold, and see if there be a-ny sor-row like un-to his

sor-row.

Recitative
He was cut off

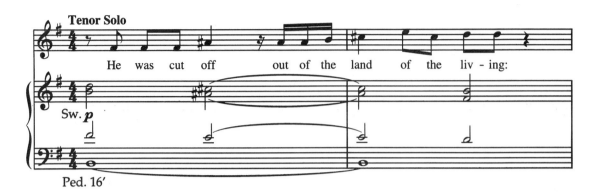

Air
But thou didst not leave his soul in hell

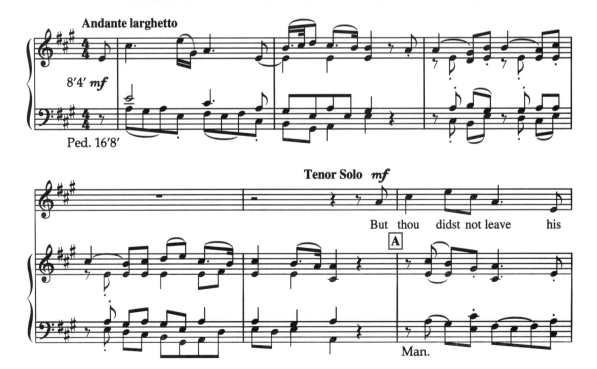

see cor - rup - tion, nor didst thou suf - fer, nor

Man. Ped.

didst thou suf - fer thy ho - ly one, thy ho - ly one to

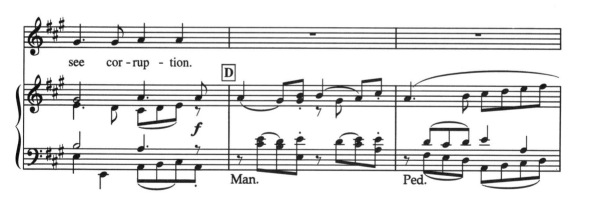

see cor - rup - tion.

D

f

Man. Ped.

Chorus
Lift up your heads, O ye gates

Lord strong and migh-ty, the Lord strong and migh-ty, the Lord migh - ty in bat-tle.

Lord strong and migh-ty, the Lord strong and migh-ty, the Lord migh - ty in bat-tle.

Lord strong and migh-ty, the Lord strong and migh-ty, the Lord migh - ty in bat-tle.

B

mf
Lift up your heads, O ye gates, and be ye lift up, ye

mf
Lift up your heads, O ye gates, and be ye lift up, ye

mf
Lift up your heads, O ye gates, and be ye lift up, ye

B

Ped.

the King of Glo - ry, the Lord of Hosts, he

is the King of Glo - ry, the Lord of

King of Glo - ry, the Lord of

is the King of Glo - ry,

Man.

is the King of Glo - - -

Hosts, he is the King of Glo - - ry, of

Hosts, he is the King of Glo - -

-ry, he is the King of Glo-ry, he is the King of Glo-ry,

-ry, he is the King of Glo-ry, he is the King of Glo-ry,

-ry, he is the King of Glo-ry, he is the King of Glo-ry,

-ry, he is the King of Glo-ry, he is the King of Glo-ry,

Ped. ad lib.

the Lord of Hosts, the Lord of Hosts, the Lord of Hosts,

the Lord of Hosts, the Lord of Hosts, the Lord of

the Lord of Hosts, the Lord of Hosts, the Lord of

the Lord of Hosts, the Lord of Hosts, the Lord of

Ped.

the Lord of Hosts,   he   is the King of Glo -   -

Hosts,   the Lord of Hosts,   he is   the King   of   Glo -

Hosts,   the Lord of Hosts,   he is   the King   of   Glo -

Hosts,   the Lord of Hosts,   he is the King of   Glo   -

-        - ry,   he   is the King of Glo - ry,   he

-     ry,   of Glo - ry,   he is the King of Glo - ry,   he

-     ry,   of Glo - ry,   he is the King of Glo - ry,   he

-        - ry,   he   is the King of Glo - ry,   he

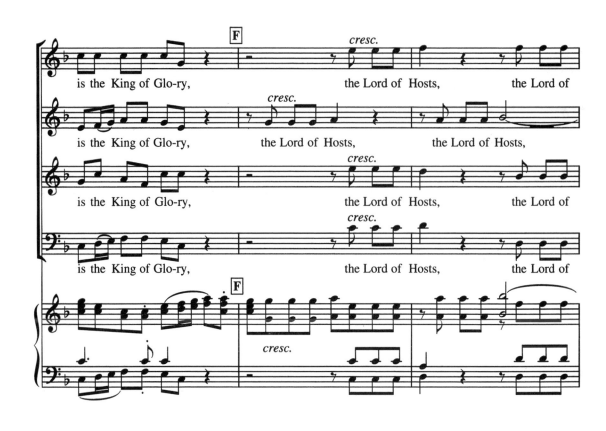

ry, the King of Glo - ry, he

ry, the King of Glo - ry, he

ry, the King of Glo - ry, he

ry, the King of Glo - ry, he

Man.

is the King of Glo-ry, he is the King of Glo-ry, of Glo - ry.

is the King of Glo-ry, he is the King of Glo-ry, of Glo - ry.

is the King of Glo-ry, he is the King of Glo-ry, of Glo - ry.

is the King of Glo-ry, he is the King of Glo-ry, of Glo - ry.

Ped.

Air
Why do the nations so furiously rage together?

ge - ther? Why do the peo - ple i - ma - gine a vain

thing? Why do the na - tions rage

so

fu - rious - ly to - ge - ther? Why

(Man. or Ped.) Ped.

do the peo-ple i - ma - - gine a vain thing, i - ma - gine a vain thing? Why do the na-tions so fu - rious-ly rage to - ge - ther? and why do the

peo-ple, and why do the peo-ple i -

ma - gine a vain thing? Why do the na - tions

rage

so fu-rious-ly to - ge-ther, so fu-rious-ly to-

C

ge - ther?   and why do the peo-ple   i - ma - gine a vain

thing,   i - ma -   gine a vain

thing?   and why   do   the peo-ple   i - ma - gine a   vain

thing?

D

ge - ther   a-gainst the Lord,   and a - gainst   his   a-

noin -

- ted,   a - gainst the Lord,   and his   a-

Gt. *f*

noin -   - ted.

Recitative
He that dwelleth in heaven

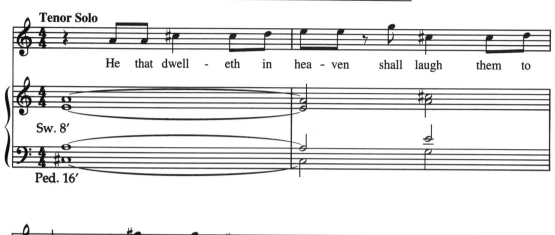

He that dwell – eth in hea – ven shall laugh them to

scorn: the Lord shall have them in de – ri – sion.

Air
Thou shalt break them

pie - ces   like   a   pot - - -

- ter's   ves - sel.

Thou shalt break them,

thou   shalt   break them   with   a   rod

thou shalt dash them in pie - ces like a

pot - - ter's ves - sel.

Hallelujah!

le - lu-jah, hal - le-lu-jah, hal - le-lu-jah, hal-le-

le - lu-jah, hal - le-lu-jah, hal - le-lu-jah, hal-le-

le - lu-jah, hal - le-lu-jah, hal - le-lu-jah, hal-le-

le - lu-jah, hal - le-lu-jah, hal - le-lu-jah, hal-le-

lu-jah, hal-le-lu-jah, hal - le-lu - jah! for the Lord

lu-jah, hal-le-lu-jah, hal - le - lu-jah! for the Lord

lu-jah, hal-le-lu-jah, hal - le - lu-jah! for the Lord

lu-jah, hal-le-lu-jah, hal - le - lu - jah! for the Lord

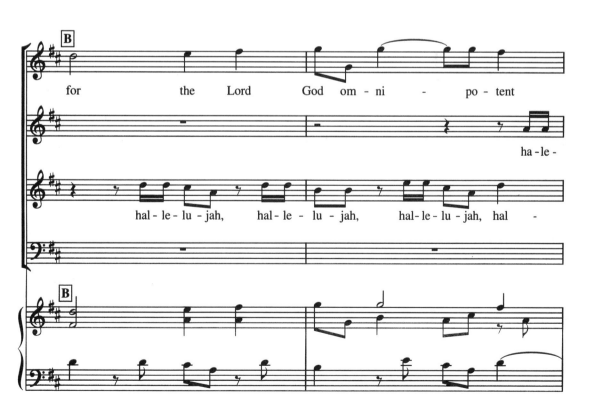

Where the text '-jah, hal-' is to be sung to one note, the two syllables should be run together.

le - lu - jah! ... The king-dom of this
hal - le - lu - jah! ... The king-dom of this
le - lu - jah! ... The king-dom of this
lu - jah, hal - le - lu - jah! ... The king-dom of this

world ... is be - come the king-dom of our Lord and of his
world ... is be - come the king-dom of our Lord and of his
world ... is be - come the king-dom of our Lord and of his
world ... is be - come the king-dom of our Lord and of his

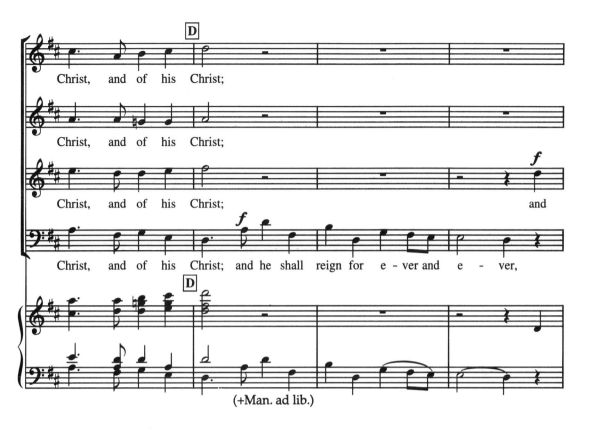

and Lord of lords,

and Lord of lords,

e -ver, hal-le-lu-jah, hal-le - lu-jah, for e-ver and

e -ver, hal-le-lu-jah, hal-le - lu-jah, for e-ver and

King of kings,

for e-ver and

e -ver, hal-le-lu-jah, hal-le - lu-jah, for e-ver and

e -ver, hal-le-lu-jah, hal-le - lu-jah, for e-ver and

(+reed)

Ped.

155

reign for e - ver, for e - ver and e - ver, King of

he shall reign for e - ver and e - ver, King of

reign for e - ver, for e - ver and e - ver, King of

reign for e - ver, for e - ver and e - ver, King of

L.H. reed

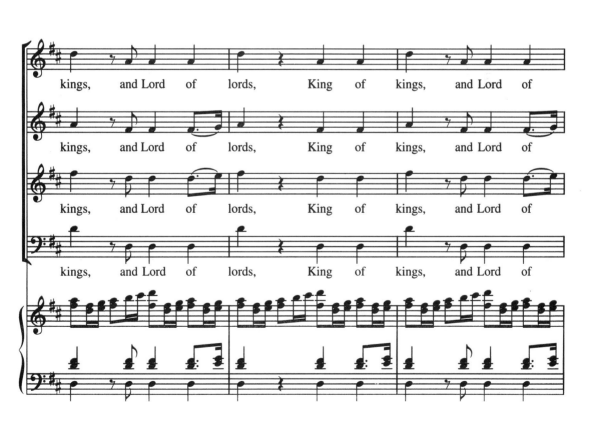

kings, and Lord of lords, King of kings, and Lord of

kings, and Lord of lords, King of kings, and Lord of

kings, and Lord of lords, King of kings, and Lord of

kings, and Lord of lords, King of kings, and Lord of

lords, and he shall reign for e - ver and e -

lords, and he shall reign for e - ver and e -

lords, and he shall reign for e - ver and e -

lords, and he shall reign for e - ver, for e - ver and e -

ver, King of kings, and Lord of lords, hal-le-lu-jah, hal-le-

ver, for e-ver and e-ver, for e-ver and e-ver, hal-le-lu-jah, hal-le-

ver, for e-ver and e-ver, for e-ver and e-ver, hal-le-lu-jah, hal-le-

ver, for e-ver and e-ver, for e-ver and e-ver, hal-le-lu-jah, hal-le-

lu–jah, hal-le-lu-jah, hal-le-lu-jah, hal - le - lu - jah!

lu–jah, hal-le-lu-jah, hal-le-lu-jah, hal - le - lu - jah!

lu–jah, hal-le-lu-jah, hal-le-lu-jah, hal - le - lu - jah!

lu–jah, hal-le-lu-jah, hal-le-lu-jah, hal - le - lu - jah!

Air
I know that my redeemer liveth

Larghetto

Gt. 8'4' *mf*

Ped. 16'

Soprano Solo

I know that my re - dee - mer li - veth,

and that he shall stand

at the lat - ter day

Man.　　　　Ped.

li - veth, and he shall stand at the lat - ter day

Ped.

u - pon the earth, u - pon the earth;

f

Man. Ped.

mp

and though worms des -

D

mp

troy this bo-dy, yet in my flesh shall

I see God, yet in my flesh shall I see

God. I know that

my re-dee-mer li-veth, and though worms des-

troy this bo - dy, yet in my flesh shall I see

God, yet in my flesh shall I see

God, shall I see God. I know that my re - dee - mer

li - veth, for now is Christ

ri - sen from the dead, the first fruits of them that sleep, of them that sleep, the first fruits of them that sleep, for now is Christ

ri - sen, for now is Christ ri - sen from the dead,

the first fruits of them, of them that sleep.

Chorus
Since by man came death

* Double voices if necessary.

al - so the re - sur - rec - tion of the dead, by man came al - so the re - sur-

al - so the re - sur-rec - tion of the dead, by man came al - so the re - sur-

al - so the re - sur - rec - tion of the dead, by man came al - so the re - sur-

al - so the re - sur - rec - tion of the dead, by man came al - so the re - sur-

B **Grave**

p

rec - tion of the dead. For as in A - dam all die, for as in

p

rec - tion of the dead. For as in A - dam all die, for as in

p

rec - tion of the dead. For as in A - dam all die, for as in

p

rec - tion of the dead. For as in A - dam all die, for as in

B **Grave**

8' *p*

Ped. 16' Man.

Christ shall all, so in Christ shall all be made a-

Christ shall all, so in Christ shall all be made a-

Christ shall all, so in Christ shall all be made a-

Christ shall all, so in Christ shall all be made a-

live, ev'n so in Christ shall all, shall all be made a-

live, ev'n so in Christ shall all, shall all be made a-

live, ev'n so in Christ shall all, shall all be made a-

live, ev'n so in Christ shall all, shall all be made a-

live.

live.

live.

live.

Recitative

Behold, I tell you a mystery

Bass Solo

Be-hold, I tell you a my-ste-ry, we shall not all sleep, but we shall all be

Sw. 8' *p*

Ped. 16''

changed in a mo-ment in the twink-ling of an eye, at the last trum-pet.

mp

mf

Air
The trumpet shall sound

and the dead shall be raised, be raised in - cor -

rup-ti-ble, be raised in - cor - rup-ti-ble,

mf
and we shall be changed,

and we shall be

changed.

C

f

Man.

f

The trum-pet shall sound, the trum-pet shall

Ped.

sound, and the dead shall be raised,

D

177

be raised in - cor - rup - ti-ble,

be raised in - cor - rup-ti-ble,

Solo

and we shall be changed, be changed,

and we shall be changed,

E

Gt.

178

and we shall be changed,

we shall be changed, and

Man.

Ped.

we shall be changed, and we shall be changed,

F

and

Man.

179

we shall be changed, we shall be changed,

and we shall be changed,

Adagio   **Tempo I**

we shall be changed.

G

Ped.

Man.

Ped.

Worthy is the Lamb that was slain

pow - er,   and   ri - ches,   and   wis - dom,   and strength,   and

pow - er,   and   ri - ches,   and   wis - dom,   and strength,   and

pow - er,   and   ri - ches,   and   wis - dom,   and strength,   and

pow - er,   and   ri - ches,   and   wis - dom,   and strength,   and

ho -nour,   and glo - ry,   and bless - ing.   Wor - thy

ho -nour,   and glo - ry,   and bless - ing.   Wor - thy

ho -nour,   and glo - ry,   and bless - ing.   Wor - thy

ho -nour,   and glo - ry,   and bless - ing.   Wor - thy

A **Largo**

f

Ped.

is the Lamb that was slain, and hath re-deem-ed us to God, to

Andante

God by his blood, to re-ceive pow-er, and ri-ches, and

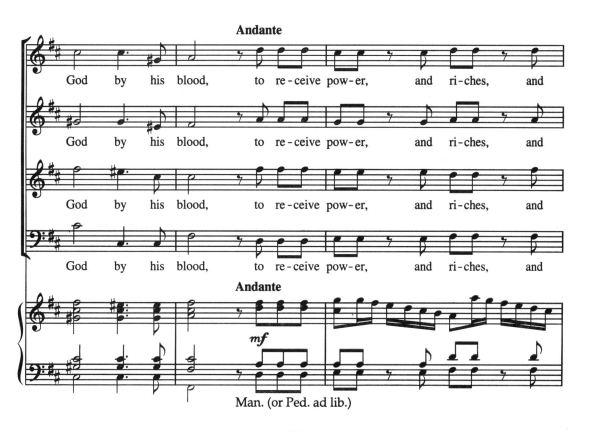

Andante

mf

Man. (or Ped. ad lib.)

wis - dom, and strength, and ho -nour, and glo - ry, and

wis - dom, and strength, and ho -nour, and glo - ry, and

wis - dom, and strength, and ho -nour, and glo - ry, and

wis - dom, and strength, and ho -nour, and glo - ry, and

B **Larghetto**

bless - ing.

bless - ing.

bless - ing. Bless - ing and ho - nour, glo -ry and

bless - ing. Bless - ing and ho - nour, glo - ry and

B **Larghetto**

Man.

Where the text '-ry and' is to be sung to one note, the two syllables should be run together.

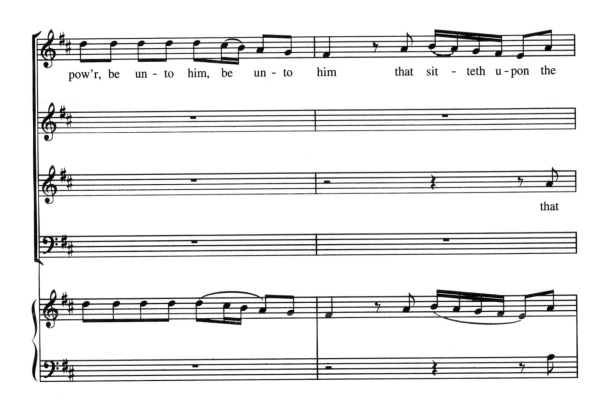

pow'r, be un - to him, be un - to him that sit - teth u - pon the

that

throne, and un - to the Lamb,

f

Bless - ing and

sit - teth u - pon the throne and un - to the Lamb,

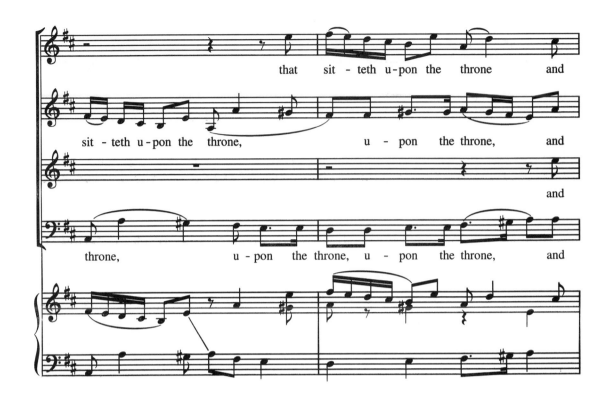

* Optional cut to ⊕, after letter D.

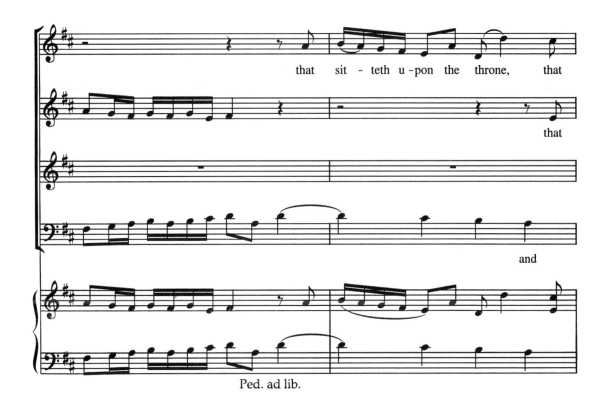

that sit - teth u - pon the throne, that

that

and

Ped. ad lib.

sit - teth u - pon the throne, for e - ver and e -

sit - teth u - pon the throne for e - ver and e -

bless - ing and ho - nour, glo - ry and pow'r, be un - to

un - to the Lamb, for e - ver and e -

glo - ry and pow - er, be un - to him that sit - teth u - pon the

glo - ry and pow - er, be un - to him that sit - teth u - pon the

glo - ry and pow - er, be un - to him

glo - ry and pow - er, be un - to him that

Man.

throne, u - pon the throne, and un - to the

throne, and un - to the

that sit - teth u - pon the throne, and un - to the

sit - teth u - pon the throne, and un - to the Lamb, un - to the

193

Lamb, for e - ver, for
Lamb, for e - ver, for e - ver, for e - ver, for
Lamb, for e - ver, for e - ver, for e - ver, for
Lamb, for e - ver, for e - ver, for

Ped. ad lib.

e - ver and e - ver, for e - ver and e - ver, for
e - ver and e - ver, for e - ver and e - ver for
e - ver and e - ver, for e - ver and e - ver, for
e - ver and e - ver, for e - ver and e - ver, for

Man.

e -ver and e -ver, for e -ver and e -ver, for

e -ver and e -ver, for e -ver and e -

e -ver and e - ver, for e - ver and e - ver, for

e - ver and e - ver, for e - ver and e -

Adagio

e - ver, for e -ver and e - ver, for e -ver and e - ver.

- ver for e -ver and e - ver, for e -ver and e - ver.

e - ver, for e -ver and e - ver, for e -ver and e - ver.

- ver, for e -ver and e - ver, for e -ver and e - ver.

Adagio

Ped.

attacca

195

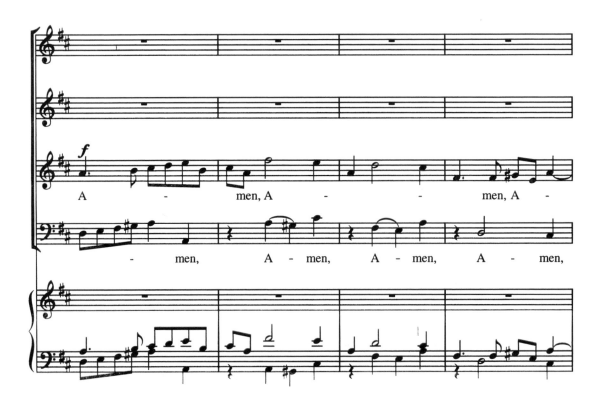

-men, A - men,

A - men, A - men, A - men,

A - men, A - men,

A - men, A - men,

Ped.   f   Man.

+2'

198

199

Ped. ad lib.

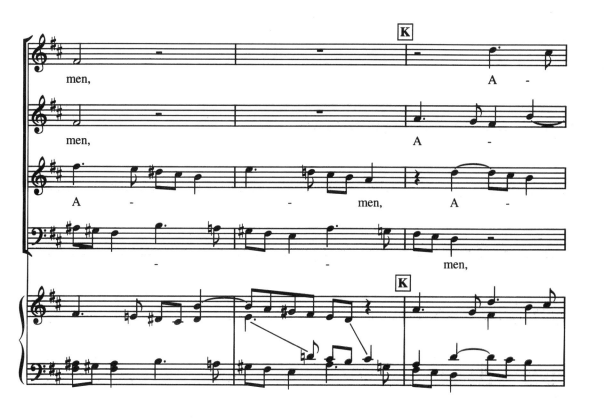

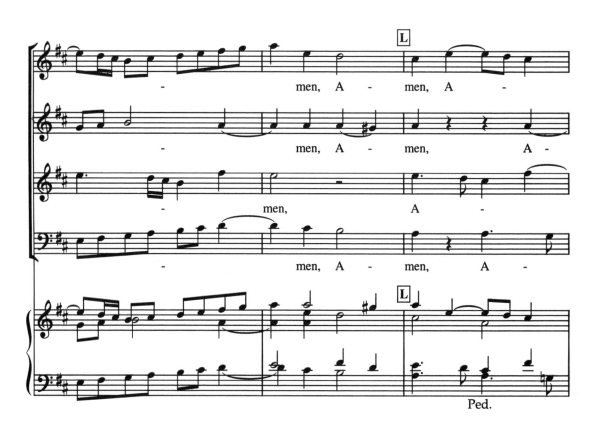

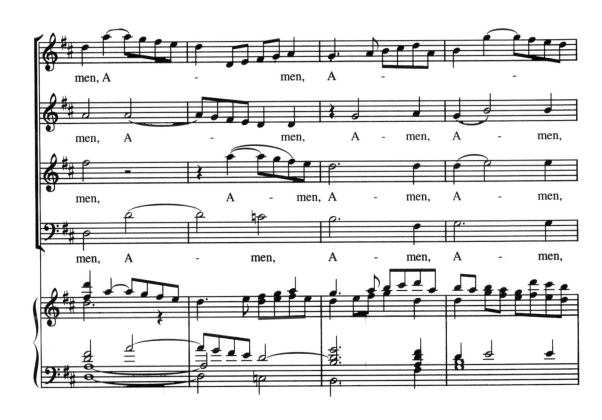

men, A - men, A - men, A - men, A - men, A - men, A - men, A - men, A - men, A - men, A - men, A - men,

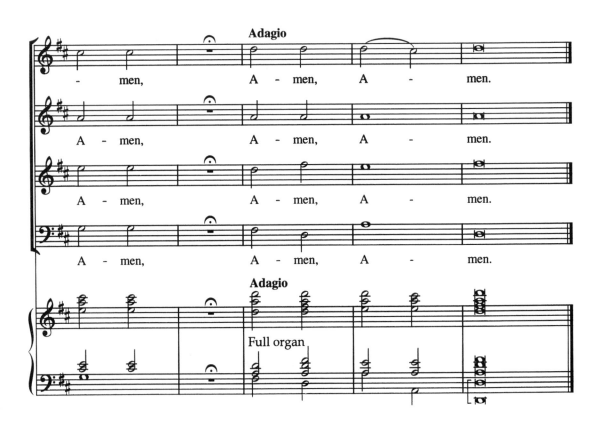

- men, A - men, A - men.

A - men, A - men, A - men.

A - men, A - men, A - men.

A - men, A - men, A - men.

Adagio

Full organ